IDEAS BAN
RE
SIKHISM

Lesley Prior

CONTENTS

Folens Publishers

How to use this book

Ideas Bank books provide ready-to-use, practical, photocopiable activity pages for children, **plus** a wealth of ideas for extension and development.

TEACHER IDEAS PAGE　　　　　　　　　　**PHOTOCOPIABLE ACTIVITY PAGE**

Clear focus on the activity.

Detailed background information to reinforce the topic.

Suggestions on how children should approach the activity.

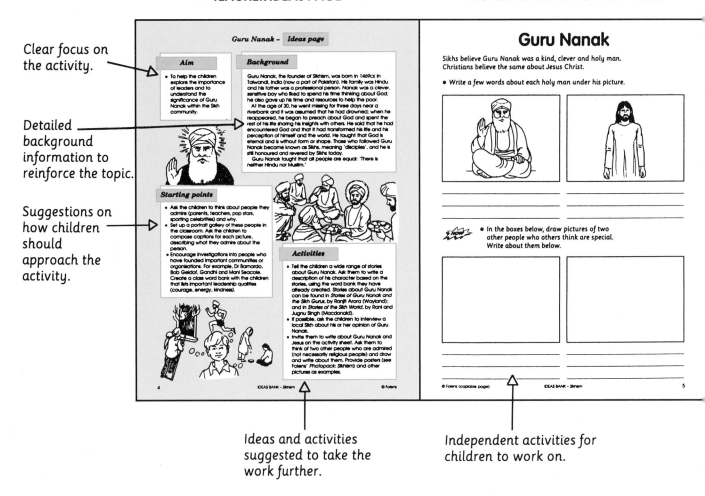

Ideas and activities suggested to take the work further.

Independent activities for children to work on.

Time-saving, relevant and practical, **Ideas Bank** books ensure that you will always have work ready to hand.

Editor: Michael Spilling.　　　　　　Layout artist: Patricia Hollingsworth.

Cover image: Zefa.　　　　　　Illustrations: Graham-Cameron Illustrations/Tony Dover.

© 1995 Folens Limited, on behalf of the author.

First published 1995 by Folens Limited, Dunstable and Dublin.

Folens Limited, Albert House, Apex Business Centre, Boscombe Road, Dunstable, LU5 4RL, England.

ISBN 1 85276 857-6

Printed in Singapore by Craft Print.

Introduction

The purpose of this book is to enable children to learn about, and learn from, Sikh beliefs, customs and practices.

The activities are designed to:
- provide the children with a context in which they can begin to explore their responses to important questions
- contribute to the children's understanding of themselves and the world.

The children's own experiences provide the starting point for this exploration. The journey of discovery is enriched and enlightened by the contributions and experiences of members of the Sikh community. The topics were selected with reference to the School Curriculum and Assessment Authority (SCAA) Model Syllabuses, a range of syllabuses produced by the Local Education Authority and in full consultation with members of the Sikh faith.

NB: Throughout Folens' *Ideas Bank: Sikhism* we have used the short forms CE (Common Era) and BCE (Before Common Era), rather than the Christian oriented AD and BC.

A glossary of useful terms is provided at the back of the book (page 48). This could be photocopied and used by the children to extend their vocabulary on Sikhism.

Sikhs are followers of the religion of Sikhism, which is one of the six main religions in the world today. It is estimated that there are about 19 million Sikhs, 40,000 of whom live in the United Kingdom. The largest Sikh community (roughly 80%) live in the northern Indian province of Punjab, where the Sikh way of life first began.

The word 'Sikh' means 'learner' or 'disciple'; Sikhs follow the teachings of the ten Gurus or religious teachers. Guru Nanak (born 1469 CE) was the first Sikh Guru and founded the faith. Sikhs believe that there is only one God and that God's teachings are revealed to them through the Sikh holy scripture, the *Guru Granth Sahib*. Sikhs believe that God is good and forgives all sins; they believe the best way to worship God is by following the Gurus and living an honest and compassionate life. Sikhs believe in racial and sexual equality, because God created and loves all humankind, regardless of creed, race, colour and gender.

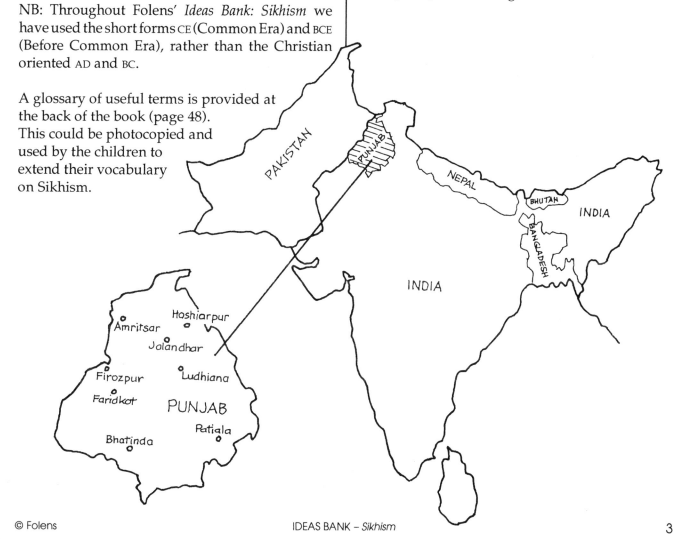

Guru Nanak – Ideas page

Aim

- To help the children explore the importance of leaders and to understand the significance of Guru Nanak within the Sikh community.

Background

Guru Nanak, the founder of Sikhism, was born in 1469CE in Talwandi, India (now a part of Pakistan). His family was Hindu and his father was a professional person. Nanak was a clever, sensitive boy who liked to spend his time thinking about God; he also gave up his time and resources to help the poor.

At the age of 30, he went missing for three days near a riverbank and it was assumed that he had drowned; when he reappeared, he began to preach about God and spent the rest of his life sharing his insights with others. He said that he had encountered God and that it had transformed his life and his perception of himself and the world. He taught that God is eternal and is without form or shape. Those who followed Guru Nanak became known as Sikhs, meaning 'disciples', and he is still honoured and revered by Sikhs today.

Guru Nanak taught that all people are equal: 'There is neither Hindu nor Muslim.'

Starting points

- Ask the children to think about people they admire (parents, teachers, pop stars, sporting celebrities) and why.
- Set up a portrait gallery of these people in the classroom. Ask the children to compose captions for each picture, describing what they admire about the person.
- Encourage investigations into people who have founded important communities or organisations. For example, Dr Barnardo, Bob Geldof, Gandhi and Mani Seacole. Create a class word bank with the children that lists important leadership qualities (courage, energy, kindness).

Activities

- Tell the children a wide range of stories about Guru Nanak. Ask them to write a description of his character based on the stories, using the word bank they have already created. Stories about Guru Nanak can be found in *Stories of Guru Nanak and the Sikh Gurus*, by Ranjit Arora (Wayland); and in *Stories of the Sikh World*, by Rani and Jugnu Singh (Macdonald).
- If possible, ask the children to interview a local Sikh about his or her opinion of Guru Nanak.
- Invite them to write about Guru Nanak and Jesus on the activity sheet. Ask them to think of two other people who are admired (not necessarily religious people) and draw and write about them. Provide posters (see Folens' *Photopack: Sikhism*) and other pictures as examples.

Guru Nanak

Sikhs believe Guru Nanak was a kind, clever and holy man.
Christians believe the same about Jesus Christ.

● Write a few words about each holy man under his picture.

_____   _____

_____   _____

_____   _____

 ● In the boxes below, draw pictures of two
other people who others think are special.
Write about them below.

_____   _____

_____   _____

The ten Gurus – Ideas page

Aims

- To enable the children to understand that a community is made up of a variety of people, each with different talents.
- To explore how each of the ten Gurus contributed to the development of Sikhism.

The ten Gurus.

Starting points

- Ask the children to think of all the people who contribute to the running of the school (teachers, cleaners, secretaries).
- Invite them to draw or photograph each person and research their different roles. Ask them to use the computer to produce a booklet about those who work in the school; add the pictures and place it in the school entrance area.
- Discuss what might happen at school if one member of staff were absent.

Background

Guru Nanak was the first of ten Sikh Gurus or leaders. He was followed by nine other men who each made their own individual contribution to the establishment of Sikhism.

Angad Dev (1504–1552)	Promoted the Punjabi language, making it available to common people.
Amar Das (1479–1574)	Established the langar, the kitchen in the gurdwara, providing poor people with a source of food.
Ram Das (1534–1581)	Built the Pool of Immortality and founded the city of Amritsar.
Arjan Dev (1563–1606)	Compiled the *Guru Granth Sahib* (the Sikh holy scriptures) and built the Harimandir, the Golden Temple, in Amritsar.
Har Gobind (1595–1644)	Fought against invaders.
Har Rai (1630–1661)	Advocated twice-daily meetings.
Har Krishnan (1656–1664)	Sometimes known as the 'boy Guru', he cared for the sick, risking his life during a smallpox plague.
Tegh Bahadur (1621–1675)	Fought against religious fanaticism and was eventually martyred for his beliefs.
Gobind Singh (1666–1708)	Established the Khalsa and proclaimed that the holy scriptures, the *Guru Granth Sahib*, would replace the living Gurus as spiritual guide of the faith.

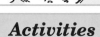

Activities

- Read or tell the children stories about the various Gurus, emphasising their different strengths and their contributions to Sikhism (for sources, refer to the books mentioned in *Activities* on page 4).
- Invite them to complete the activity sheet, matching each Guru with the correct attribute.

Development

- Guru Nanak once said, "There is no Hindu and no Muslim ... I shall follow God's path." He deplored the divisions that exist between people of different faiths. Ask the children to think of places where people are divided because of their religious beliefs and invite them to debate why this may be so.

The ten Gurus

Each of the ten Gurus helped develop
Sikhism in different ways.

- Match each Guru with what he did.

Guru
Nanak

Guru Angad
Dev

Guru Amar
Das

Guru Ram
Das

Guru Arjan
Dev

Guru Har
Gobind

Guru Tegh
Bahadur

Guru Har
Krishnan

Guru Har
Rai

Guru Gobind
Singh

| encouraged the use of Punjabi | set up the langar system | produced the Guru Granth Sahib |

| founded Sikhism | established the Khalsa | fought invaders | held religious gatherings |

| established Amritsar | cared for the sick | wanted freedom in the way people worship |

- Think of something important that you
  have done and write about it.

Guru Gobind Singh – Ideas page

Aim

- To help the children understand the significance of Guru Gobind Singh for the Sikh community.

Background

Guru Gobind Singh (1666–1708CE) was the last of the ten living Gurus. It was on Baisakhi day in 1699CE that he founded the Khalsa, the 'community of the pure'. He began by asking who amongst the gathering of Sikhs was willing to die for their faith. One by one, five Sikhs stepped forward into the Guru's tent; on each occasion a swishing sound was heard, followed by a thud – they had apparently been killed by the Guru with his sword. When Gobind Singh reappeared with the five unharmed volunteers, he explained to the crowd that this had been a test of their courage and willingness to die for their faith. These Sikhs had passed the test and became known as the Panj piare, the 'five beloved ones'. Gobind Singh then performed the first Amrit ceremony (see page 36), initiating Sikhs into the Khalsa. It was he who first insisted that Sikhs adopt the Five Ks (see page 10). Before he died, he declared that the Sikh scriptures, the *Guru Granth Sahib*, would take his place and that there should be no more living Gurus.

Starting points

- Ask the children to interview their head teacher about his or her role as leader in the school; what qualities do they need to carry out the job successfully?
- Invite them to interview local religious figures about their roles as leaders within their own communities. Ask them to produce an imaginary job description for a priest, a rabbi, or an imam, listing the essential qualities for the successful applicant.

Guru Gobind Singh made some fundamental contributions to the development of Sikhism, including introducing the wearing of the Five Ks, performing the first ever Amrit ceremony and declaring that the Guru Granth Sahib would take his place as a spiritual focus.

A priest must be:
good
kind
patient
forgiving
helpful

- Ask them to find out about contemporary religious leaders. For example, they could research a day in the life of the Pope, the Archbishop of Canterbury and the Chief Rabbi.

Activities

- Encourage the children to learn as much as possible about the life and character of Guru Gobind Singh through stories, interviews with Sikhs and library research.
- Ask the children to discuss what happened at the foundation of the Khalsa, using the descriptions beneath the boxes. Were the five volunteers killed and brought back to life? Or were they not killed at all?
- Ask them to design and make a card to send to a Sikh who is celebrating the birthday of Guru Gobind Singh in January.

Guru Gobind Singh

Below is the story of the Khalsa, when Guru Gobind Singh first initiated the Sikh people into the new religion.

● In the blank boxes, draw pictures that describe the scene.

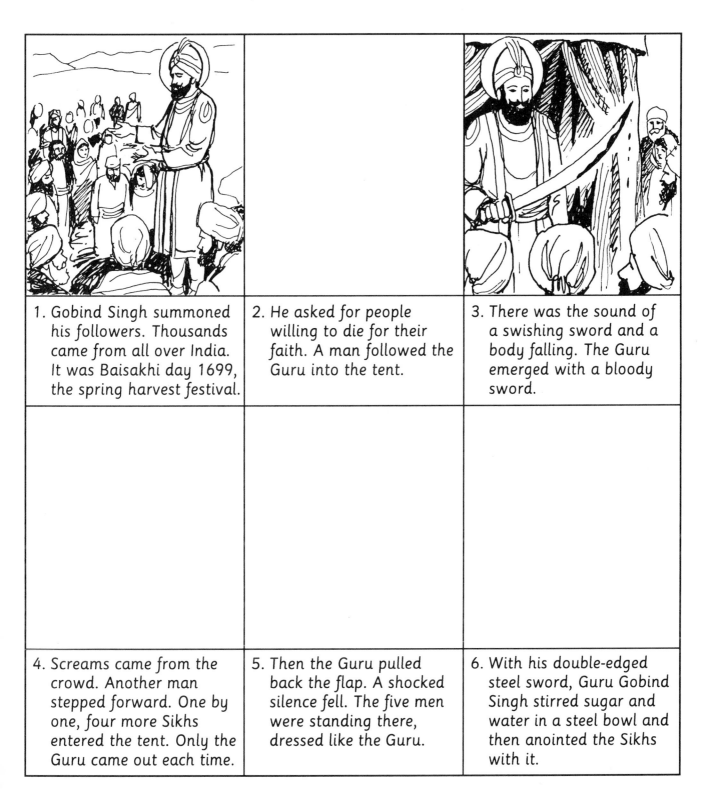

1. Gobind Singh summoned his followers. Thousands came from all over India. It was Baisakhi day 1699, the spring harvest festival.	2. He asked for people willing to die for their faith. A man followed the Guru into the tent.	3. There was the sound of a swishing sword and a body falling. The Guru emerged with a bloody sword.
4. Screams came from the crowd. Another man stepped forward. One by one, four more Sikhs entered the tent. Only the Guru came out each time.	5. Then the Guru pulled back the flap. A shocked silence fell. The five men were standing there, dressed like the Guru.	6. With his double-edged steel sword, Guru Gobind Singh stirred sugar and water in a steel bowl and then anointed the Sikhs with it.

The Five Ks – Ideas page

Aim

- To explore why people in some religions choose to express their identities through outward symbols and how this is expressed within the Sikh community.

Starting points

- Discuss with the children ways that they are recognised as members of their particular school community, encouraging them to focus particularly on the uniform, badge or logo. They can create a display in the school entrance area, showing examples.
- Ask them to collect photographs, magazine and newspaper pictures, books and postcards showing a wide range of different uniforms (for example: Brownies, ambulance crew, soldiers, waiters/ waitresses, refuse collectors). Include some examples of religious costumes (a Buddhist nun, a Greek Orthodox priest, a Sikh). Discuss how different uniforms convey messages about those who wear them.
- Construct a game where the children match pictures of various uniforms to descriptions (verbal or written) of what they signify and the roles of those who wear them. Make a class book on uniforms.

Background

In 1699CE on Baisakhi day, a Hindu spring festival, Guru Gobind Singh established the Khalsa. The Khalsa, which means 'community of the pure', constituted the first initiation ceremony for the new Sikh community. Guru Gobind Singh invited people to commit themselves to the Sikh faith and to express this commitment by adopting certain outward symbols. These symbols are known as the Five Ks and are worn by both men and women. Sikhs who have been initiated through the Amrit ceremony are referred to as 'Khalsa Sikhs' and wear the Five Ks. In Punjabi, the language spoken by many Sikhs, each of the words begins with the equivalent of the letter K.

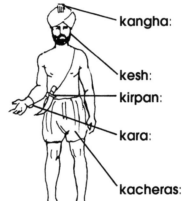

kangha: a metal or wooden hair comb to signify a neat and orderly way of life

kesh: uncut hair as a symbol of purity

kirpan: a short sword to remind Sikhs to fight against evil

kara: a steel bracelet, usually worn on the right wrist, symbolising the eternity of God

kacheras: shorts worn as underwear to symbolise chastity

Activities

- Show the children pictures of the Five Ks, or if possible, the artefacts themselves. Discuss their meaning for Sikhs. The activity sheet gives children the opportunity to demonstrate their understanding.
- Make a chart of artefacts and clothes used in other religions.

Islam				
Christianity	cross			
Buddhism				
Hinduism				
Judaism		skull cap		

- If possible, invite a local member of the Sikh community to talk to the children about the meaning of the Five Ks; a male Sikh may be willing to demonstrate how he ties his turban.
- Invite the children to debate how a young Sikh might face problems at school because he or she wears the Five Ks. Ask them how these difficulties might be resolved.

The Five Ks

- Read the captions about the Five Ks.

- Draw the pictures that match correctly with the captions. One has been done for you.

This is worn on the wrist and reminds Sikhs that God has no beginning and no end.	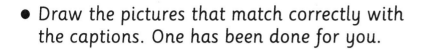
This reminds Sikhs that they should be ready to resist bad things.	
This reminds Sikhs that they should be neat, clean and tidy.	
Many Sikhs have their hair like this to show that they are a special group of people.	
Sikhs wear these special clothes made from cotton.	

 • Find some things that people in other religions like to wear.

IDEAS BANK – *Sikhism*   11

Nam japna (meditation on God) –

Aim

- To explore the advantages of meditation and reflection and to discover how this is practised in the Sikh community.

Background

Khalsa Sikhs are expected to spend part of each day meditating on the name of God. He or she should find a quiet place and sit comfortably on the floor. It is believed that meditation helps Sikhs develop a deeper relationship with God, thus bringing peace of mind. The words 'Raheguru, Raheguru ...' (meaning 'wonderful Lord') are repeated over and over again in order to increase concentration and focus thought. Meditation offers the devout Sikh an opportunity to reflect on those things that are important to him or her; it is time for an individual to become less self-centred and more God-centred.

Prayers such as the *Mool Mantar* – the main Sikh prayer found in the *Guru Granth Sahib* – may also form a focus for reflection and thought; other extracts from the scriptures are sometimes used in the same way. Some Sikhs use prayer beads during meditation. Each bead represents a recitation of 'Raheguru'. Holding the beads in the hand is felt by some Sikhs to be useful for focusing attention.

Starting points

- Ask the children to think of times and places when they are expected to be still or quiet; for example, in a library, in an examination and during collective worship. Ask them to design posters for display in these various locations, requesting quiet and giving reasons why this is necessary.
- Invite the children to design and set up a 'thinking corner' in the classroom. Encourage them to think about suitable colour schemes, furniture, pictures, artefacts and books.
- Ask them to write about or draw the places they go to when they wish to be alone to think quietly.

Activities

- Before handing out the activity sheets, ask the children to think of words to describe someone they admire – perhaps a religious leader or a sporting personality. Brainstorm and record their words.
- Explain to the children that many Sikhs like to spend time each day thinking about God, whom they describe as 'Raheguru', or 'wonderful Lord'. Ask them to sit in silence. Give them the activity sheet, then ask them to suggest other adjectives Sikhs might use to describe God, such as kind, powerful and gentle.

Developments

- Ask the children to find out where people of other religions go to pray.
- Research the different prayers used in other religions.
- Write a prayer suitable for one of the religions.

IDEAS BANK – *Sikhism*   © Folens

Thinking about God

This Sikh is thinking about God. Sikhs call God 'Raheguru', which means 'wonderful Lord'.

- Can you suggest any other words she might use to describe God?

- In the space below, write a prayer or poem for Sikhs about God, using the words you have chosen.
- Decorate your prayer.

Kirat karna (earning an honest living) — | Ideas page

Aim

- To encourage the children to evaluate their attitudes to work through an exploration of the Sikh notion of Kirat karna.

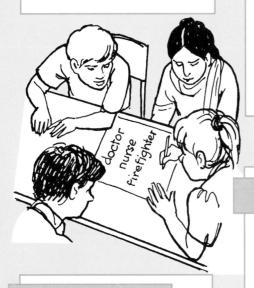

Starting points

- Ask the children to think of ways that people can provide for themselves – either honestly or dishonestly – and discuss which of these ways is acceptable and why.
- Draw up a list of as many different professions as possible and include the different characteristics of each. Set up a computer database using this information.
- Challenge them to imagine that they have been asked to put together a team of ten people from different professions to travel to a disaster area to offer help. Discuss with the class which professions they think should be represented in the group and why.

Background

Practising Sikhs are expected to work hard and earn an honest living. Guru Nanak taught that it is wrong to take things that rightfully belong to others: Sikhs should provide for themselves. For this reason many Sikhs have entered some of the traditional professions, becoming teachers, doctors, dentists, civil servants and so on.

> NB: It is important to be sensitive to those children who may have had experience of family unemployment.

> Dear Jim,
> Thank you for your letter asking me about my job as a pharmacist. As a Sikh, it is important to me to help other people: by giving them medicine to make them better, I feel I am doing something very useful...

Activities

- Inform the children about the Sikh concept of Kirat karna. Ask them to interview Sikhs (either in person or by letter) about the jobs that they do and why. Do they feel their work is in keeping with the Sikh ideal?
- On the activity sheet, ask the children to write why these jobs are in keeping with Sikh tradition.

Doctor	Helps people to get well.
Police officer	Makes sure people are safe.
Teacher	Helps children to learn about the world.
Solicitor	Helps people resolve legal difficulties.

- Set up an investigation into the kinds of jobs that would be acceptable to people who belong to other religious traditions and store the information on a classroom database.

Development

- Do a class survey to find out what kinds of jobs the children want to do and why. What influences have made them decide?

A good job

● Look at the people below. In the boxes, write why they are suitable jobs for Sikhs.

Doctor	Police officer

       _____
       _____
       _____
       _____

_____

Teacher	Solicitor

● On a separate piece of paper, draw pictures and write about other jobs that are suitable for Sikhs.

IDEAS BANK – *Sikhism*

Vand chhakna *(sharing with others)* – Ideas page

Aim

- To encourage the children to explore the ways in which they share with others and how charity is practised and expressed within the Sikh community, especially through the langar.

Starting points

- Ask the children to think of what they share with others (sweets, toys, crayons, information, cassette tapes, compact discs) and why they do this. Invite each child to write a resolution about sharing more with others. Collate these into a class book.
- Challenge them to identify a local, national or international charity. Let them choose a cause and support it in a practical way. For example, they could support the annual *Blue Peter* programme appeal or collect jumble to help the school's PTA.

Background

Charity is fundamental to Sikhism. Sikhs practise this mainly through giving to the poor and sharing resources with those less fortunate than themselves.

All gurdwaras are open to everyone, regardless of race, class or creed. The langar, a kitchen in the gurdwara, serves daily vegetarian meals for the whole community; meals are also free for all visitors. All members of the community contribute to the langar by either donating food or money. Both men and women help prepare the meal.

The Sikh community not only provides for itself, but helps people outside the community. For example, during the miners' strike of the early 1980s, food parcels were sent to the miners' families by a London gurdwara.

Activities

- Explain to the children what a langar is, describing how everyone is welcome to share the vegetarian meal. If possible, visit a local gurdwara to see the langar. Those sharing the meal are expected to make a contribution to the community.
- Ask them to plan a meal for the whole class. They should consider resources (ingredients, equipment, skills, tasks). Remind them that all the children in the class should be able to share in the meal, whatever their dietary requirements and preferences.

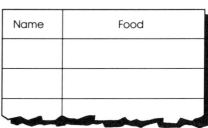

Name	Food

- Ask the children to design a menu card for the day of the meal.
- Arrange a visit to a non-Sikh place of worship in your area. Invite the children to interview members of the relevant community about their views on charity; what kind of help do they provide?

Sharing

- Everyone has a job to do at the langar. Here are some of the different jobs.

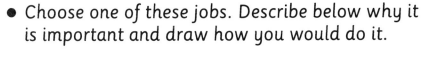

buying food

preparing the food

cleaning the tables and floor

serving the food

washing up

clearing up

- Choose one of these jobs. Describe below why it is important and draw how you would do it.

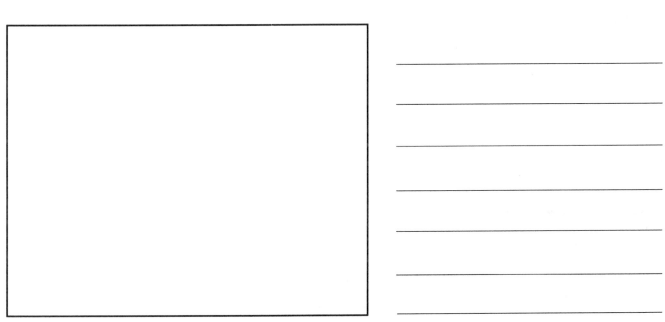

 ● Design a menu for a langar meal.

Sewa (service to others) – Ideas page

Aim

- To encourage the children to think about the importance of serving others and how this is expressed in the Sikh religion.

Real learning is serving others.

Starting points

- Invite the children to devise a scheme for sharing their time and skills. For example, they could help a local charity, work to support younger children in the school, organise a dog-walking service in their community and so on.
- Let them to contact the local library to find out more about voluntary organisations in your area; what support do they offer to others through their work?
- Encourage them to set up interviews with people who work on a voluntary basis and to ask questions about how they see their role.

Background

Practising Sikhs are expected to devote themselves to a life of service: they should not only serve other people, but also the Gurus and God. This ideal is probably best expressed in the story of Bhai Khanaya.

Bhai Khanaya was a soldier in the army of Guru Gobind Singh. One day, after a terrible battle had been fought, he was found wandering among the sick and wounded on the field. One of his fellow soldiers noticed that he was giving water not only to the injured Sikhs, but also to members of the enemy army! His companion was horrified and rushed to the Guru to complain about what he had seen. The Guru thought quietly for a moment or two and then said how impressed he was by the kindness of Bhai Khanaya. The Guru recognised in his compassionate behaviour a man who served all of humanity, as well as God and his Guru. Gobind Singh then ordered that soothing ointment should be given to all those who had been wounded on the battlefield, whether friend or foe, thus endorsing Bhai Khanaya's actions and asserting the Sikh tradition of service to others.

Development

- Ask the children to set up displays in the classroom that focus on famous people who have lived to serve others. For example, Dr Barnardo, Mother Theresa and St Margaret of Scotland.

Activities

- Discuss how Sikhs might choose to practise Sewa in their own lives. If possible, contact a gurdwara and discover how members of the Sikh community give their time and skills to help others; for example, in assisting building work, in raising funds, or by offering Punjabi lessons.
- Ask the children to complete the activity sheet. Encourage the children to think about how they might serve others.

Helping others

- How are these people helping others?
  Under each picture, write what you think.

- Are any of them connected with a religion?

- Could any of them be Sikhs?

Red Cross

RSPCA

_____

_____

_____

_____

_____

_____

Salvation Army

Cancer research

_____

_____

_____

_____

_____

_____

 • What could you do to serve others?

Mool Mantar (main Sikh prayer) – Ideas page

Aims

- To explore the importance of words as an aid to reflection and prayer.
- To encourage children to understand the significance of the *Mool Mantar* for Sikhs.

Background

The *Guru Granth Sahib*, the Sikh holy book, opens with the words of the first hymn composed by Guru Nanak. These words are known as the *Mool Mantar* and Sikhs are expected to recite them daily. It provides a basic outline of Sikh belief and is a key feature of both public and private worship. The *Mool Mantar* is considered the essence of Sikh theology and has pride of place in the *Guru Granth Sahib*.

The *Mool Mantar* expresses the Sikh belief in one God. They believe God is without beginning or end and is omnipresent. While it may be impossible for the human mind to ever attain a full understanding of God, Sikhs believe God will always love and protect them. The Gurus' role is to help Sikhs understand and experience God more fully, both through prayer and in their daily lives.

IK ONKAR   SAT NAAM   KARTA PURKH

NIR BHAU   NIR VAIR   AKAAL MOORAT

AJOONI SAIBHANG   GUR PARSAAD

The Mool Mantar: *written in Punjabi script and translated into the Roman alphabet.*

Ik Onkar sign
This is the opening verse of the Mool Mantar *and means, 'There is only one God.' Sikhs sometimes wear this symbol as a badge.*

Starting points

- Ask the children to choose their favourite pieces of writing (stories, poems, songs, prayers). They should explain the reasons for their choices.
- Invite them to copy and decorate their favourite piece in their best handwriting. Make the results into a class book or wall display.

PRAYER BOARD

Activities

- Read the *Mool Mantar* with the children; explain that it is a special prayer for Sikhs. Invite the children to discuss its possible meaning.
- Ask the children to think of something or someone that they or others might like to pray about. Those children who want to could write a prayer and perhaps illustrate it. These could be pinned on a prayer board in sealed envelopes.
- Set up investigations into famous prayers of other religions (for example, the *Lord's Prayer* and the *Salah*) or any words that inspire. Discuss their possible meanings, then desktop publish these on the school computer.

Prayer

The words of this prayer are important to most Sikhs.
It is very special and should be beautifully illustrated.

● Draw a decorative border around the Mool Mantar.

Mool Mantar

There is only one God
Truth is his name
He is the creator
He is without fear
He is without hate
Immortal and without form
He is beyond birth and death, the enlightened one
He can be known by the Guru's grace.

● Write about something that a Sikh might want to pray for.
For example, when a friend is ill.

The gurdwara (1) – Ideas page

Aim

- To help the children explore the importance of religious buildings in the life of a community and understand the significance of the gurdwara for many Sikhs.

Background

Gurdwara means 'doorway to the Guru' and is the Sikh place of worship. Gurdwaras may not look similar: it is not the style of the building that is important but the function that it serves. The gurdwara is essentially a place where Sikhs can meet together in the presence of the *Guru Granth Sahib*. Gurdwaras always contain a room for worship where the scriptures are the main focus; the book is placed on a takht, or raised platform, covered by a canopy. There are no chairs and the men and women sit on the floor in separate areas. Anyone worshipping in the prayer hall will be offered karah parshad, sanctified food, a custom that helps create a sense of community and welcome.

Starting points

- Encourage the children to list local buildings that are used by the community: for example, libraries, sports centres, theatres, restaurants and schools. Can they identify the services that each building provides?
- Ask them to write about occasions when they have gathered together with their family and friends. Why did the gathering take place and what happened?
- Let them plan a special gathering for members of their class. They should organise entertainment, refreshments and decorations. The gathering could be to celebrate the end of term, an anniversary, a birthday or a national holiday.

The Guru Granth Sahib.

Activities

- If possible, take the children to a local gurdwara and investigate how it is used by the Sikh community.
- On the activity sheet, ask the children to draw or write down the different ways that Sikhs use their gurdwaras.
- Make karah parshad with the children and discuss the significance of everyone sharing the same food at the gurdwara. In the gurdwara, karah parshad is made sacred when a special prayer, the *Japji Sahib*, is recited over the food while it is being stirred. In the classroom karah parshad will not have been blessed in this way, but can be eaten by all the children, regardless of their beliefs.

Karah parshad

You will need:
110 gms unsalted butter
55 gms plain flour
110 gms semolina
$\frac{3}{4}$ pint of water and 110 gms sugar boiled together

Melt the butter in a saucepan over a low heat and then add the flour, mixing well with a wooden spoon. Pour in the semolina and beat well, heating the mixture until the butter separates. Gradually add the sugared water and mix vigorously until a paste is formed.

Place of worship

● In the boxes, draw or write four different ways that
Sikhs use a gurdwara, their place of worship.

1.

2.　　　　To sing

3.　　　To learn Punjabi

4.

 ● With your teacher, make karah parshad.

The gurdwara (2) – Ideas page

Aim

- To help the children explore ways that buildings are created to meet particular needs and how this occurs in the design of gurdwaras.

Background

In Britain, where the Sikh community is growing and becoming more established, gurdwaras are being built to specific requirements. They include all the traditional features: a main prayer hall, a langar hall with kitchen and storage facilities, communal meeting areas and a room for private devotions. Outside the gurdwara stands the Nishan Sahib (the Sikh flag). Worshippers and visitors are expected to remove their shoes and cover their heads: a storage area is usually provided for footwear.

Starting points

- The children could – as individuals, pairs, groups or the whole class – draw up a plan of their school and classroom. Discuss what they think are the good and bad points of the design. Encourage them to think about how the space is used and whether the design is well planned.
- Ask them to draw or describe in writing their ideal school and classroom. They should explain their reasons for incorporating their chosen features.

Activities

- Set up investigations into the design features of a gurdwara. Can the children explain the purpose of each feature? For those who cannot visit a gurdwara, Staffordshire LEA (tel. 01785 223121) produces the useful *Places of Worship Pack*, by Margaret Griffin and Paul Bellingham.
- On the activity sheet, invite the children to draw a design for a new gurdwara, showing a floor plan and/or front elevation.
- In small groups, ask the children to write the different sections of a gurdwara magazine. They could give details of various events: services, Punjabi language classes, sporting events (such as hockey) and talks. The children could use a desktop publishing package to facilitate editing.

Development

- What does a gurdwara have in common with other religious buildings?

The Nishan Sahib.

	Prayer hall	Kitchen	Meeting room	Shoe storage	Place for holy book
Sikhism					
Buddhism					
Judaism					
Islam					
Christianity					
Hinduism					

Design a gurdwara

A local Sikh community has asked you to design a new gurdwara.
A gurdwara may include the following:

prayer hall	Nishan Sahib	Guru Granth	a private room
langar hall	(the Sikh flag)	Sahib	storage area for
	meeting area	kitchen	shoes

● In the space below, draw your design, including all the key features.

IDEAS BANK – *Sikhism*

Amritsar and the Harimandir –

Aim

- To encourage the children to explore why particular places are important to some groups and to help them understand the significance of Amritsar for the Sikh community.

Background

Amritsar is a city in the state of Punjab in north-eastern India. The city was founded by the fourth Guru, Ram Das, in 1577CE. The city is revered and visited by many Sikhs because of its historic, cultural and religious significance. Many Sikhs go to Amritsar to visit the most important of all gurdwaras, the Harimandir (temple of God), familiarly known as the 'Golden Temple'. It was built in the time of the fifth Guru, Arjan Dev, and is surrounded by the Pool of Immortality. The pool is said to have great healing powers. The foundation stone was laid by a Muslim saint, Mian Mir, in 1588CE. On completion of the temple building Guru Arjan Dev installed the *Guru Granth Sahib*.

The Harimandir is first and foremost a place of worship, but also bears witness to centuries of Sikh tradition and culture. The Golden Temple is part of a large complex and has been described as the 'nerve centre' of Sikhism. It is exquisitely designed and decorated: the central dome of the temple is covered in gold leaf. Many Sikhs bathe in the pool before entering the Harimandir, where there are continuous readings from the *Guru Granth Sahib*.

Starting points

- Ask the children to think about famous buildings in the world. They could collect data and produce graphs to show which are the best-known and which they most admire.
- Encourage the children to collect, produce and display pictures or models of famous buildings. For example: the Taj Mahal, the Eiffel Tower, the Sydney Opera House, the Empire State Building and the Houses of Parliament.

- Ask the children to discuss the functions of these buildings and the reasons why people wish to visit them.

Activities

- Set up an interest area in the classroom about the Harimandir featuring posters, photographs, video film, souvenirs and children's work (useful resources could be gained through writing to the Indian Tourist Board or can be found in Beryl Dhanjal's book, *Amritsar*).
- On the activity sheet, ask the children to write a message describing an imaginary first visit to the Harimandir.

Development

- Set up investigations into other famous religious buildings: the Dome of the Rock, Saint Peter's in Rome and so on. Find out why these buildings are considered important.

A visit to the Golden Temple

● Imagine that you are a Sikh. You are about to visit the
Harimandir for the first time and you are very excited.

● On the postcard, write a message to a friend about your visit.

Family life and the home – Ideas page

Aim

- To enable the children to explore their own family lives and to encourage them to understand the characteristics and role of family life in the Sikh community.

Sikh homes are often decorated with images of Guru Nanak.

Background

Family life is extremely important for Sikhs. Guru Nanak said, 'Living within the family life, one realises God.' For practising Sikhs, the day begins with a bath followed by meditation on the name of God. Prayers are also recited or perhaps sections of the scripture, like the *Mool Mantar*. Many Sikh homes will be decorated with pictures of the ten Gurus or the Harimandir as reminders of Sikh teaching and identity. Some homes might feature a copy of the *Guru Granth Sahib*: this must be kept in a special room. The whole family will gather for prayers in the presence of the book every morning and evening.

Sikhs believe in sexual equality: men and women share equally in daily tasks and family life. The majority of Sikhs in Britain have their origins in the Punjab in northern India, so Punjabi customs, food and styles of dress may feature strongly in their lives without necessarily having any religious significance.

NB: The teacher should be aware that not all children may come from happy, well-balanced home environments and that family life could be a sensitive issue to some of them.

Starting points

- Ask the children to monitor their daily class routines for one week and record them in a diary: play times, lunch times and PE lessons.
- Prepare long, narrow strips of card and make them into zig-zag books. Mark each section with different times of the day; ask the children to write or draw what they were doing at each of those times on one particular day and discuss and compare the results.

Sikh families gather together to meditate on the words of the Guru Granth Sahib.

Activities

- Through interviews, video library books and other resources, help the children research the daily routine of a Khalsa Sikh. Encourage them to be aware of similarities to and differences from their own family routines. Can they suggest reasons for these differences?
- Ask the children to cut out the pictures on the activity sheet and place them in the correct order on a strip of card. They could also add captions to describe each picture.

Development

- Find out about where families belonging to other religions keep their holy book.

A typical day

- Look at the pictures describing what this Sikh girl does each day.

- Cut out the pictures and put them in the correct order to show her daily routine.

- Write about or draw pictures to show your ideal day. Compare your ideas with those of your partner.

The Guru Granth Sahib – Ideas page

Aim

- To make the children aware why some books have particular significance and to teach them why the *Guru Granth Sahib* is important in the Sikh community.

While reading the Guru Granth Sahib *the granthi usually waves a chauri, a fan made of nylon or yak hairs, over the book as a sign of authority.*

Background

The *Guru Granth Sahib* is a collection of writings assembled by Guru Arjan Dev. It contains the teachings of the first five Sikh Gurus plus some sections written by Hindus and Muslims sympathetic to Sikh teachings. The *Guru Granth Sahib* focuses on the individual's quest to deepen and develop their relationship with God. It is written in ancient Punjabi, a language often difficult for modern Sikhs to understand.

Since the death of the tenth Guru, Gobind Singh, the *Guru Granth Sahib* has been revered as the main source of guidance for members of the community and is respected like a living Guru. In the gurdwara it has the place of honour and Sikhs show that they honour the teachings by bowing low before it. Each night the book is taken from the main prayer hall and literally 'put to bed' in an adjacent room. Early each morning, it is returned to the prayer hall in a special procession. On important occasions, all 1430 pages may be read at one sitting, using a series of readers. This is called an Akhand Path and lasts for about 48 hours.

The Khanda symbol
The centre of the symbol is a double-edged sword, signifying God's almighty power. The 'Chakra', or the circle, symbolises continuity. The two outer swords represent the spiritual and political balance in the Universe.

Starting points

- Invite the children to collect as many different examples of reading matter as possible: newspapers, magazines, comics, instruction manuals, books and other religious texts. Can they explain why people want to read these different books?
- Ask them to carry out a survey of favourite books: at home, in class and throughout the school. Display some of the children's favourite books.
- Ask them to explain, either verbally or on paper, their choice of reading matter and encourage them to discuss whether the books have had any influence on their lives.

Activities

- Give the children as much information as possible about the *Guru Granth Sahib*; explain how it is revered within the Sikh community and discuss the reasons why. Useful resources are: *Holy Books*, by Jon Mayled (Wayland), and *The Guru Granth Sahib*, by Piara Singh Sambhi (Heinemann).
- The pages of the *Guru Granth Sahib* are often decorated with beautiful patterns. On the activity sheet, ask the children to surround the writings with an appropriate patterned border. Make the completed sheets into a book that can be placed in the classroom book corner or school library as an informative resource for others.

The holy book

- Here are some writings from the Sikh holy book, the Guru Granth Sahib.
- Decorate the pages and make them into a book. Draw a Khanda sign on the cover.

You are a tree;
your beautiful branches
are everywhere.

Who made the stars
that twinkle in the
midnight sky?
Who made the sun?
Who made the moon?
Whose light is all
around me?

Who makes the waves
rise up from the sea?
Who makes the seeds
sprout and grow?
Who ripens the fruit on
the trees?

You are very dear to me,
as dear as milk is to the
baby,
as the flower is to the
humming bee,
as the pond is to the fish.
as I need water on a hot
day,
I need you.

 • Make your own special book.

IDEAS BANK – *Sikhism*

Stories of Guru Nanak – Ideas page

Aim

- To understand how stories convey meaning and to examine examples from the Sikh tradition.

Background

Guru Nanak, like the other nine Gurus, is not worshipped by Sikhs, but is honoured and respected by them. He is regarded as an exceptional human being and many stories about him reinforce this view by emphasising his unique qualities and status. Here are some examples:

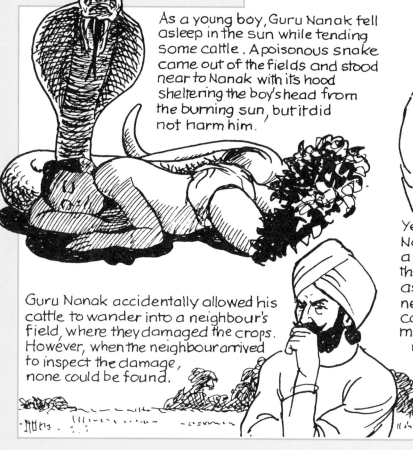

As a young boy, Guru Nanak fell asleep in the sun while tending some cattle. A poisonous snake came out of the fields and stood near to Nanak with its hood sheltering the boy's head from the burning sun, but it did not harm him.

Guru Nanak accidentally allowed his cattle to wander into a neighbour's field, where they damaged the crops. However, when the neighbour arrived to inspect the damage, none could be found.

Years later, as a great teacher, Guru Nanak visited the home of Duni Chand, a rich and proud merchant. He gave the merchant a needle as a gift, asking him to return it to him in the next world. Duni Chand was initially confused by Nanak's gesture. After much thought, he realised that nothing material could be taken into the next world. He saw the worthlessness of material goods and subsequently gave up all his possessions to help the poor.

Starting points

- Collect stories about famous people and important religious figures (Jesus, the Buddha, Muhammad) and read these to the children. Discuss with them how the stories show the unique qualities of each individual. For example, Mozart was already an accomplished composer at a very young age.
- Divide the children into groups and ask them to select one incident from the life of a famous person. Ask them to role-play the incident.

  NB: The Sikh Gurus must not be depicted in any role play.

Activities

- Collect and read stories about Guru Nanak and ask the children to write them in their own words and illustrate them (for sources use the books listed under *Activities* on page 4). You could then construct a class biography of the Guru.
- On the activity sheet, ask the children to write the story alongside each picture.

Stories of Guru Nanak

● Here are pictures of three stories about Guru Nanak.
Write what the story is about next to each picture.

 ● In the Bible, find the story about Daniel. How is it the
same as or different from stories about Guru Nanak?

IDEAS BANK – *Sikhism*

The naming ceremony – Ideas page

Aim

- To introduce the children to the Sikh naming ceremony.

At a Sikh naming ceremony, a kirpan is dipped in Amrit and offered to the child.

Background

A few weeks after a birth, mother and child go to the gurdwara for the naming ceremony. Close relatives usually attend. The parents thank God for the child and choose its name. The *Guru Granth Sahib* is opened at random and the hymn that appears on the left-hand page is read by the granthi, a reader of the sacred scriptures who officiates at ceremonies. The first letter of the chosen hymn becomes the first letter of the child's name; the name is then selected by the parents. Sikh names are unisex and usually have a specific meaning. In addition to a personal name, boys are given the name 'Singh', meaning 'lion'; girls are given the name 'Kaur', meaning 'princess'. These may be used instead of, or in addition to, a family name.

Activities

- Introduce the children to the Sikh naming ceremony using books, posters (see Folens' *Photo Pack Sikhism*), slides, video film and interviews with local Sikhs.
- Ask each child to create an illuminated letter of their own initial and to think of as many other names as possible that begin with the same letter.

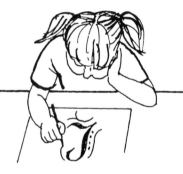

Starting points

- Ask the children to conduct a survey of names in their class or school; they should establish which are the least popular and which are the most popular.
- Each child could choose a new name and write about the reasons for their choice.
- Ask the children to find out why they were given their name. Were they named for religious reasons (for example, after a saint or a holy man) or after a relative or famous person?

Developments

- Set up investigations into other naming ceremonies and customs surrounding the birth of a baby.
- Find names that are common in particular religions and record them on a chart.

Judaism	Ruth	David
Islam	Ali	
Hinduism	Krishnan	

- On the activity sheet ask children to suggest their ten favourite names and the reasons why they chose them. If possible, they should include some Sikh names.

Different names

- How did you get your name? Does it have a special meaning?

- Choose your ten favourite names and say why you chose them.
  Include both boys' and girls' names.
  Try to include some Sikh names, if you can.

	Name	Reason
1.		
2.		
3.		
4.		
5.		
6.		
7.		
8.		
9.		
10.		

NOW ● Draw a picture of a naming ceremony in another religion.

The Amrit ceremony – Ideas page

Aim

- To help children explore how responsibilities increase as they grow older and to consider how this affects members of the Sikh community.

Starting points

- Ask the children to identify and analyse the differences between adulthood and childhood. They could summarise their findings in written or pictorial form or through drama and role-play.
- Ask them to research the different ways that the passage from childhood to adulthood is marked. For example, passing a driving test, beginning a job, leaving home and having a child. Collate their findings in a class book.

- Invite them to write poems about childhood and adulthood that focus on the positive and negative aspects of both stages in life. Display these in the classroom.

Background

The Amrit ceremony can occur at any time during a person's adult life and marks a special level of commitment to the Sikh faith; not all Sikhs make this commitment. The service is witnessed by five people who have already undergone the ceremony. They symbolise the five faithful who were willing to lay down their lives for Guru Gobind Singh. The participants gather in front of the *Guru Granth Sahib* and prayers are recited; sweets are mixed with water to make amrit, which means 'nectar'.

This mixture is drunk by each candidate and is also used to anoint them. They must promise to wear the Five Ks, recite daily prayers, never use tobacco or alcohol, never commit adultery and never eat meat.

Activities

- Invite the children to research and investigate the key elements of the Amrit ceremony: the setting, the participants, the artefacts used, the clothes worn, the promises that are made and why. With the class, explore the reasons why intoxicants such as alcohol and nicotine are not acceptable to Sikhs.
- Set up investigations into other ceremonies that mark entry into a particular group (such as Cubs, Brownies) and other religious initiation rites.
- On the activity sheet, ask the children to identify behaviour that fulfils the promises made at Amrit, as well as that which does not. Encourage them to explore the reasons for these practices; how do they compare with other religions? Are they similar?

The Amrit ceremony

- Look at the pictures. Which of these people have fulfilled the promises made in the Amrit ceremony?

- Write underneath each one why you think so.

_____

_____

_____

_____

_____

_____

_____

_____

_____

_____

_____

_____

- What rules do people of other religions have to obey? Are they similar to those found in Sikhism?

The marriage ceremony – Ideas page

Aim

- To explore why many couples choose to affirm their commitment to one another through marriage and how this is practised within the Sikh community.

Starting points

- Discuss with the children the reasons why people get married. A debate could follow on the advantages and disadvantages of both love matches and assisted marriages.
- Ask the children to plan and present role-plays of a young couple who hope to marry for love debating these issues with a couple advocating arranged marriages.
- Ask the children to suggest some suitable promises for a bride and groom to make to signify their commitment.

Background

Marriage is seen as the foundation of the Sikh family. The service, called Anand karaj (ceremony of bliss), must take place in the presence of the *Guru Granth Sahib*. Any Sikh can officiate at the ceremony, and is chosen by both families.

The bridegroom will arrive at the gurdwara (or another appointed place), accompanied by his relatives and friends. After a prayer, they will be welcomed by the family of the bride. Often, the bride and groom will exchange garlands before taking their places in front of the *Guru Granth Sahib*. The bride is usually dressed in lavishly embroidered red clothes (red is considered lucky) and will wear lots of jewellery, while the groom always wears a red or pink turban. The bride and groom are joined together with a chuni, or scarf, to symbolise their union. The granthi reminds the couple of their duties to each other, their families and their community. Four verses of the wedding hymn, the *Lavaan*, are recited while the couple walk together, clockwise, around the holy scriptures. Flower petals are scattered during the final verse. Prayers and readings close the service. Karah parshad is served to everyone in the langar hall followed by a celebratory meal.

Activities

- Arrange to visit a gurdwara to see where Sikh weddings take place. Show the children the *Guru Granth Sahib* and the langar hall and explain their significance in the wedding service. Ask them to complete the activity sheet to show this.
- Plan and perform a mock Sikh wedding, with the children acting the roles of bride, groom, granthi, family members and so on.
- Encourage the children to design clothes for a Sikh bride and groom.
  A useful resource might be: *Marriage Customs,* by Anita Compton (Wayland). *Eggshells and Thunderbolts* is a useful video resource package for primary RE (BBC/Culham College Institute) that includes a mock Sikh wedding.

A Sikh wedding

- Look at the five picture squares.
  Think of ways these items might feature in a Sikh wedding.

- Match the captions to the pictures to make your own information sheet about a Sikh wedding.

granthi

The bride and groom must be married in the presence of this special Sikh book.

gurdwara

This is shared with everyone at the end of the ceremony.

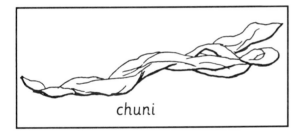
chuni

This is used to show that the bride and groom are joined together.

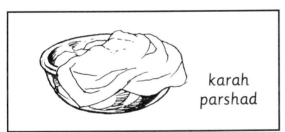
karah parshad

This person must be chosen by both families to perform the ceremony.

Guru Granth Sahib

This kind of building is often used for a Sikh wedding.

- Write a description of a Sikh wedding, mentioning the items named above.

Death and funerals – Ideas page

Aim

- To help the children discuss and explore attitudes to death and to understand how it is viewed within the Sikh community.

Starting points

- Introduce and discuss the topic of death. Read *Badger's Parting Gifts* by Susan Varley (Picture Puffin), which deals with how Badger is remembered by his friends. Teachers should take particular care with any children who have been recently bereaved.
- Ask the children to collect and examine obituaries from local and national newspapers. Can they identify common elements?

Development

- Explore what other religions believe about reincarnation and life after death.

Background

Sikhs regard death as being like falling asleep. Just as sleep brings refreshment for the day ahead, death brings rebirth in a new life. Through God's help, a Sikh may eventually become good enough to dwell with God for ever and thus end the cycle of reincarnation, of death and rebirth. This can be achieved not only by doing good deeds, but also through loving God and reflecting on his nature. Sikhs do not believe that fasting or penance will win merit for the future.

Following a death, the *Sohila* or bedtime prayer is recited and the body is washed and dressed in white. The body is adorned with the Five Ks before being placed in a coffin. Cremation follows and the ashes of the deceased are scattered on running water. A simple service at the gurdwara may also take place and langar will be served to all the mourners. After the funeral there is often a complete reading of the *Guru Granth Sahib*; the mourning period is considered over once this reading is completed. Sikhs do not erect monuments over the remains of the dead and anniversaries of a death are not commemorated.

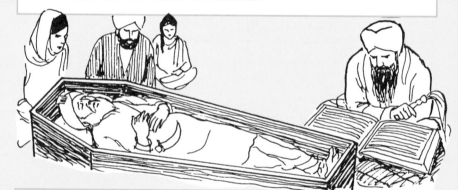

Activities

- Investigate Sikh beliefs about death and the ceremonies that surround it; ask the children to present their findings in individual or group booklets. A useful resource is *Death Customs* by Lucy Rushton (Wayland).
- On the activity sheet, ask the children to write how they would like to be remembered in years to come.
- Research death ceremonies of other major world religions. The children could also explore the differing attitudes of various cultures towards death.

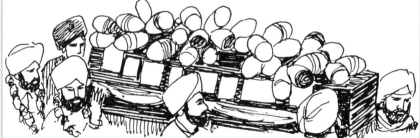

All about me

- How would you like to be remembered?
  Write about yourself, highlighting your particular achievements.

My childhood

The jobs I will have done

My family

My interests

 • Write about what you would like to achieve.

Baisakhi – Ideas page

Aim

- To enable the children to explore the importance of celebrations within their own communities and the particular significance of Baisakhi for Sikhs.

Hockey is a popular sport played at Baisakhi.

Background

The festival of Baisakhi is usually celebrated on the 13th of April. It was originally a Hindu festival marking the new harvest, but gained a new significance for Sikhs in 1699CE when Guru Gobind Singh conducted the first Amrit ceremony on that day. Today, many Sikhs still choose to receive Amrit and be admitted to the Khalsa at Baisakhi. It is also seen as a New Year celebration for Sikhs.

Sikhs prepare for the festival by taking a bath and putting on new clothes. Special food is eaten and services are held at the gurdwara. The Nishan Sahib outside the gurdwara is replaced with a new one and the flagpole is washed. An Akhand Path, a continuous reading of the *Guru Granth Sahib*, is usually arranged 48 hours before Baisakhi so that it is completed on the day itself. Sporting competitions, such as hockey matches, are usually held. Langar is served to all those taking part in the ceremonies.

The community replaces the Nishan Sahib.

Starting points

- Ask the children to list as many different kinds of celebration as possible: for example, birthday, house-warming, Easter, Ramadan and Christmas.
- Create a display about celebrations, featuring cards, invitations, decorations, menus and photographs. Identify some of the elements common to a wide range of celebrations: for example, family gathering together, special food, giving of presents and the wearing of new clothes or costumes.

A classroom display about celebrations.

Activities

- Set up investigations into the Sikh celebration of Baisakhi and invite the children to create a classroom interest area featuring their own work as well as posters, books and artefacts.
- Let them design new outfits for an imaginary Sikh family to wear on Baisakhi. These could be produced as drawings, collages or as cut-out dolls.
- Obtain a tape of bangra music and encourage the children to dance to it! (Bangra is the traditional dance form at Baisakhi time.)
- On the activity sheet, ask the children to design a card for Sikhs to send to one another on Baisakhi Day.

A greetings card

- Imagine that you are a designer for a company that makes cards. Design a card for people celebrating Baisakhi. You can use Sikh symbols like the ones on this page.

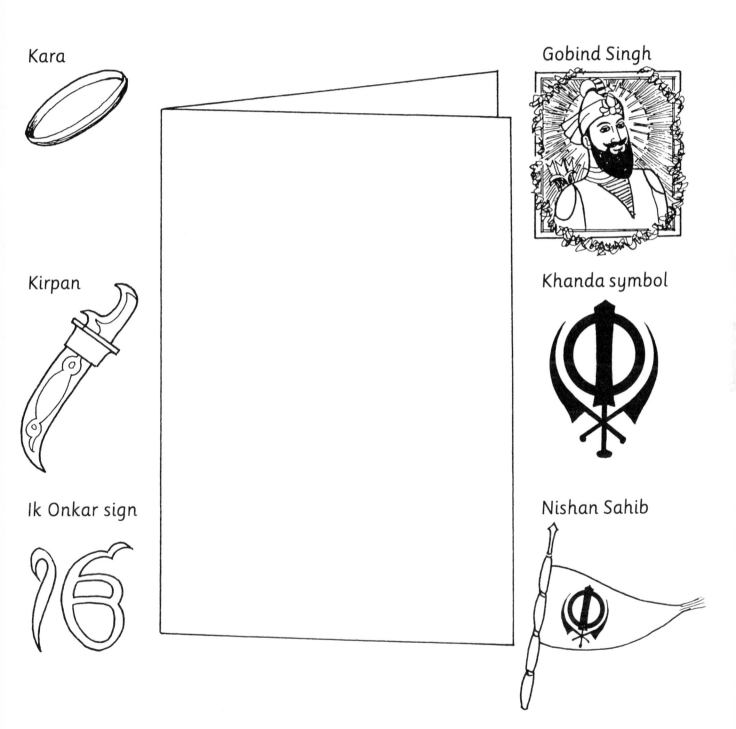

Kara

Gobind Singh

Kirpan

Khanda symbol

Ik Onkar sign

Nishan Sahib

 ● Design a card for someone celebrating success in exams, a new job or a new home.

Divali – Ideas page

Aim

- To help the children understand the importance of freedom through an exploration of the significance of Divali for Sikhs.

Starting points

- Collect, read and discuss stories that feature people who have been wrongly imprisoned. For example, from fairy stories, accounts from history and contemporary news. You might want to mention the Bosnian hostage crisis of 1995, or the Beirut hostages of the 1980s.
- Through drama, mime and role-play encourage the children to explore the trauma of being imprisoned. Invite the children to write poems, produce artwork and create dances on the theme of imprisonment. They should present these to one another.
- Discuss the kinds of celebrations that are held when prisoners are released.

Background

Divali – the Festival of Lights – is celebrated in November by both Hindus and Sikhs, but with a different emphasis.

For Hindus, the Divali celebration commemorates the safe return of Rama and Sita after various trials and dangers.

Sikhs mark the occasion because Guru Har Gobind (the sixth Guru) was released from prison on that day. He had been imprisoned for defending the weak and defenceless against the emperor. Later, the emperor was persuaded that it was wrong to keep such a spiritual and politically powerful man captive and offered him his freedom. However, Guru Har Gobind refused to leave unless he could take with him 52 others who had also been wrongly imprisoned. The emperor said that only those who could hold on to the hem of the Guru's robe would be allowed to leave with him. Unknown to the authorities, the Guru had a special robe made with 52 tassels, so that all 52 prisoners would be able to follow him to freedom! When he arrived in Amritsar, many homes were decorated with lights to celebrate his return.

Sikhs celebrate Divali by spending time with family and friends, eating special food, exchanging cards and gifts and letting off fireworks! Homes and gurdwaras are decorated with divas (small lights). These lights symbolise the triumph of good over evil and promise hope for the future.

Activities

- Read or tell the Sikh Divali story to the children and discuss ways in which Sikhs celebrate the festival.
- On the activity sheet, invite the children to decorate the picture of the Golden Temple with drawings of coloured lights; Sikhs do this to celebrate Divali. Remind them of how their own school is decorated at Christmas time, or perhaps for the harvest festival, or for sports day.
- Encourage them to write and perform a play about Divali. They could then present it to the rest of the school.

Divali

At Divali time, the Golden Temple is decorated by Sikhs.

- Decorate the picture of the Golden Temple, to show how it might look at Divali time. Remember that Divali is called the 'Festival of Lights'.

- In the space below, draw how you would decorate your classroom for a special festival.

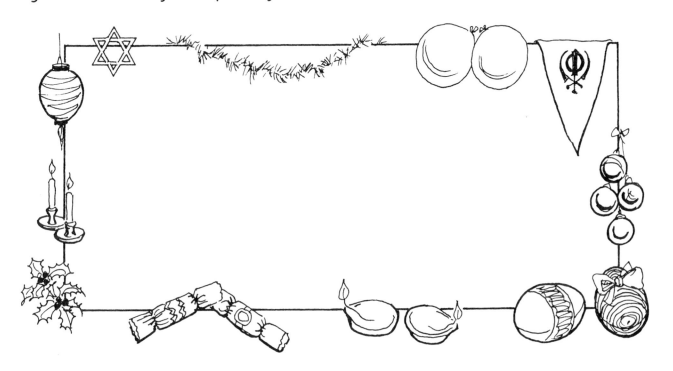

 • Make a list of times when your home is decorated.

IDEAS BANK – *Sikhism*   45

Gurpurbs – Ideas page

Aim

- To evaluate the importance of birthday celebrations and how this is reflected in the Gurpurbs of the Sikh community.

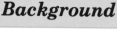

Starting points

- Tell the children some stories about birthdays. Ask them to discuss their own and other people's birthday celebrations. Can they identify common features, such as cards, presents, food and a party? Useful resources might be: *Mr Rabbit and the Lovely Present* by Charlotte Zolotow (Picture Puffin), and *The Railway Children* by E Nesbitt (Puffin), which include sections on birthdays.
- Make a wall-chart that gives the date of the birthday of each member of the class.
- Encourage the children to contribute to a class area on birthdays. They might include items such as cards, presents, photographs, invitations and party bags.

Gurpurbs Contents:
Procession
Akhand Path
Langar

Background

The birthdays of the Sikh Gurus and the anniversaries of their deaths are commemorated by many Sikhs. These occasions are called Gurpurbs. The birthdays of the first Guru, Nanak, and last Guru, Gobind Singh, are celebrated universally. Those of the other Gurus are celebrated by groups and communities that have special links with them.

Special prayers and services are held and sometimes processions are organised. The *Guru Granth Sahib* is often carried in the procession, which is led by five Sikhs meant to represent the Panj piare. Langar is served and there may be collections for charitable causes. An Akhand Path usually forms the main feature of the celebration: a non-stop reading of the *Guru Granth Sahib*, which can last up to 48 hours.

Sikh boys' pipe bands march in a procession to celebrate the Gurpurbs.

Activities

- Set up investigations into how the birthdays of famous people and religious figures are marked. For example, Queen Elizabeth, Jesus Christ and media personalities.
- Ask them to create a display board for the entrance area of the classroom informing people about one of the Gurpurbs. Explanatory leaflets can be produced on the school computer to accompany the display.
- On the activity sheet, ask the children to look at the picture of Guru Nanak and suggest reasons why Sikhs today still celebrate his birthday.

Celebrating birthdays

- Look at the picture of Guru Nanak.

- What kind of man do you think he was?
  Does he look kind, gentle and wise?

- Write below some reasons why Guru Nanak's
  birthday is still celebrated.

 • How do you celebrate your birthday?

Glossary

Akhand path — A continuous reading of the *Guru Granth Sahib* from beginning to end, often lasting 48 hours.

Amrit — Literally means 'nectar'. Sanctified liquid made of sugar and water, used in the Khalsa ceremony.

Anand karaj — The Sikh wedding ceremony, known as the 'ceremony of bliss'.

Baisakhi — A major Sikh festival celebrating the formation of the Khalsa in 1699CE.

Bhai Khanaya — A Sikh commended in battle by Guru Gobind Singh for helping the enemy wounded.

Chauri — Symbol of the authority of the *Guru Granth Sahib*. Made of yak hairs or nylon, this fan is waved over the scriptures.

Chuni — Scarf used in Sikh wedding ceremony.

Granthi — A reader of the *Guru Granth Sahib*, who officiates at ceremonies.

Gurdwara — A Sikh place of worship. Literally means the 'doorway to the Guru'.

Gurpurb — The anniversary of the birth of a Guru.

Guru — This means 'teacher'. The title of Guru is reserved for the ten human Gurus and the *Guru Granth Sahib*. It is important to note that the title 'Guru' must be used with all the Gurus' names.

Guru Amar Das — The third Guru; he established the langar.

Guru Angad Dev — The second Guru, who promoted the Punjabi language.

Guru Arjan Dev — The fifth Guru, who was the first Sikh martyr.

Guru Gobind Singh — The tenth and final Guru; he established the Khalsa.

Guru Granth Sahib — The primal collection of Sikh scriptures, compiled by Guru Arjan and given its final form by Guru Gobind Singh.

Guru Har Gobind — The sixth Sikh Guru. He fought bravely against invaders.

Guru Har Krishnan — The eighth Guru. Known as the 'boy Guru'; he cared for the sick during a smallpox plague.

Guru Har Rai — The seventh Guru.

Guru Nanak — The first Guru and the founder of the Sikh faith.

Guru Ram Das — The fourth Guru; he built the Pool of Immortality.

Guru Tegh Bahadur — The ninth Guru, who was martyred for his religious tolerance.

Ik Onkar — This means 'There is only one God.' It is the first character of the *Mool Mantar*.

Japji Sahib — A morning prayer, composed by Guru Nanak, which forms the first chapter of the *Guru Granth Sahib*.

Kachera — Traditional Sikh underwear. One of the Five Ks.

Kakka — The Five Ks.

Kangha — A comb worn in the hair. One of the Five Ks.

Kara — Steel band worn on the right wrist. One of the Five Ks.

Karah parshad — Sanctified food distributed at Sikh ceremonies.

Kaur — This means 'princess'. This name was given to all Sikh females by Guru Gobind Singh (see **Singh**).

Kesh — Uncut hair. One of the Five Ks.

Khalsa — 'The community of the pure.'

Khanda — The double-edged sword used in the initiation ceremony. Also used as an emblem on the Nishan Sahib.

Kirat karna — Earning one's livelihood by one's own efforts.

Kirpan — The Sikh word for 'sword'. One of the Five Ks.

Langar — This means 'Gurus' kitchen'. It includes the gurdwara dining hall and the food served in it.

Mool Mantar — The basic statement of belief at the beginning of the *Guru Granth Sahib*.

Nam japna — Meditation on the name of God.

Nishan Sahib — The Sikh flag flown at all gurdwaras.

Panj piare — This means 'The five beloved ones.' It refers to both those first initiated into the Five Ks and those who perform the rites today.

Punjab — 'Land of the five rivers.' The area of India where Sikhism originated.

Raheguru — This means 'wonderful Lord'. A Sikh name for God.

Sewa — Service to God, the Gurus and humanity in general.

Sikh — This means 'learner' or 'disciple'. A person who believes in the ten Gurus and the *Guru Granth Sahib*, and who has no other religion.

Singh — This means 'lion'. The name given to all Sikh males by Guru Gobind Singh.

Takht — Raised platform in a gurdwara where the *Guru Granth Sahib* is placed.

Vand chhakna — Sharing one's time, talents and possessions with the less fortunate.